A BIRTHDAY VISIT TO DR. BONES

A BIRTHDAY VISIT TO DR. BONES

Dr. Eli Ahdoot

Tintero Publishing, LA.
www.tinteropublishing.com

ISBN: 978-17352007-9-8
Formatting: Tintero Publishing
Written by: Dr. Eli Ahdoot

Print in the United States of America

Dedicated to our precious daughter, **Sienna Shira Ahdoot**, who listens to my imaginative work-related stories and encourages me to continue to help people every day. Happy 3rd Birthday! We love you endlessly and hope to provide you with a life filled with knowledge, compassion, happiness and love!

🖤

Dr. Eli Ahdoot

It was Zoey's Birthday and she was turning three. She jumped up and said, "Yay!" Because she knew it was going to be a wonderful day!

Zoey woke up so happy as Mom brought her a princess tiara in bed. Mom smiled brightly as she put it on Zoey's little head.

Zoey wore her new tiara to her sister's room.
Her sister clapped and was so happy over her new present!

Happy birthday to you,

Happy birthday to you,

Happy birthday
dear Zoey...

Happy birthday
to you!

Zoey and her sister then went to the kitchen to eat birthday cake while mommy rested and took a tea break. This was a birthday so very fine! And everything was happening right on time!

After eating so many pieces of cake, Zoey and her sister also took a break. They started to jump on the couch. Up and down, up and down! With Zoey's sparkling tiara crown!

Mom told Zoey and her sister to stop jumping because they can get an ouchie. "Please, be careful. You are each so very special!"

But then Zoey bumped into her sister and fell off the couch! Mom ran in as Zoey cried, "Ouch!"

Zoey hurt her elbow and couldn't move at all. She was curled up into a bit of a ball!

Mom took Zoey to the doctor and Zoey was scared.

But everyone was so very nice and cared a lot.

Dr. Bones came to see Zoey and examined her elbow that day.

He even took her to get a very special X-ray!

Dr. Bones put a pink cast on Zoey's arm and said it would work "like a charm." And then he gave her a cuddly teddy. "All right," he said, "now you're ready!"

Zoey went to school the next day, and everybody started to color on her cast. She was so happy and was having a blast!

Zoey felt special since turning three and really liked Dr. Bones, who was so nice and kind. A doctor with a big heart and a very smart mind!

Zoey was happy now finishing her cake. Her arm did not hurt, not even an ache. "I love you, Mom," she said. And Mom kissed her on the head and said, "Happy Birthday my beautiful Princess!"

Written by

Dr. Eli Ahdoot

Made in the USA
Las Vegas, NV
07 May 2022

48556152R00024